GLOBE FEARON'S

Skills for Independent Living

CRITICAL THINKING WORKBOOK

Globe Fearon Educational Publisher
A Division of Simon & Schuster
Upper Saddle River, New Jersey

Globe Fearon's Pacemaker Curriculum Workbooks

American Government
American Literature
Basic English
Basic Mathematics
Biology
Careers
Economics
English Composition
General Science
Health
Practical English
Practical Mathematics for Consumers
Pre-Algebra
Skills for Independent Living
United States Geography
United States History
World Geography and Cultures
World History

Project Editors: Ann Clarkson and Keisha Carter
Senior Editor: Karen Bernhaut
Production Editor: Alan Dalgleish
Electronic Page Production: Mimi Raihl and Heather Roake
Cover Design and Interior Illustration: Armando Baez
Editorial Assistant: Ryan Jones
Cover Photo: Marjory Dressler

ISBN 0-8359-3478-0

Printed in the United States of America

10 9 8 7 6 5 4 3   01 00 99 98

Globe Fearon Educational Publisher
A Division of Simon & Schuster
Upper Saddle River, New Jersey

TABLE OF CONTENTS

Introduction

What is Critical Thinking?

Critical thinking means using information that you have learned. Imagine that you are in a supermarket. You want to buy a can of soup, but you don't know which brand to choose. You may look at the prices of the different brands. You may also consider the ingredients, calories, and vitamins in each. You then evaluate the information and make a choice. You have just used critical thinking skills. Critical thinking is the act of taking information and using it in a meaningful way.

The activities in this workbook go with your Globe Fearon Pacemaker textbook. They ask you to use four different types of critical thinking skills. The four types are analysis, application, evaluation, and synthesis. You have used these skills many times in your daily life. Now you will be applying these skills to what you will learn in *Skills for Independent Living*.

The activities labeled Application ask you to use information to solve a problem or complete a task. For example, imagine that you have just learned how to read advertisements for housing. You may be asked to apply that information and write a newspaper ad for an apartment.

The activities labeled Analysis ask you to look closely at information and think about all of its parts. For example, you may be asked to look at a bank statement and answer questions about the different parts of it.

Some of the workbook activities are labeled Synthesis. In these activities you will take parts of information and create a whole. For example, you may be given a list of goals and be asked to create a plan for meeting those goals.

You will also find activities labeled Evaluation. These activities ask you to make a judgment about certain information. For example, you may be given a situation and asked to evaluate the decisions that were made. Think back to the supermarket described at the beginning of this page. As a shopper, you evaluated information about the different kinds of soup in order to make a choice.

Your textbook is a wonderful source of knowledge. By studying it, you will learn a great deal of information about skills you will need to live on your own. The real value of that information will come when you put it to use by thinking critically.

Exercise 1   Application   **Considering Qualities**

Name _____ Date _____

With a group, read the situation below. Then answer the questions that follow. Share your group's answers with the class.

Juan thought fishing was boring, but his dad loved to fish. Juan's 16th birthday was two weeks away. His father said, "I have a great idea, Juan. For your birthday, why don't we spend the whole weekend fishing, just you and me. That sounds great, doesn't it?"

Juan didn't know what to say. Two of the qualities that guided his life were honesty and concern for others. He had to decide what to do.

1. If honesty is the most important quality to Juan, what might he say to his father?

   _____

   _____

   _____

2. If concern for others is the most important quality to Juan, what might he say to his father?

   _____

   _____

   _____

3. If you were Juan, what might you say to your father?

   _____

   _____

   _____

4. What are some times when honesty might not be the best policy?

   _____

   _____

   _____

Exercise 2 Evaluation   **Sorting Out Choices**

Name _____ Date _____

Read the situation below and help Tanya make a wise decision.

Tanya had been working at a frozen yogurt shop for two weeks. One evening she was helping another employee named Kathy to clean up after the store closed.

Kathy said, "My friend is waiting for me. Let's just rinse these mixers off and put them away. No one will know whether we really cleaned them or not. I want to get out of here!"

Tanya knew a dirty mixer could cause problems. People who ate yogurt from a dirty mixer might get sick. Tanya had to decide what to do.

With a partner, discuss Tanya's choices and their possible results. Write your comments below.

1. Choice A: Put the mixers away dirty and say nothing.

    Possible results: _____

    _____

2. Choice B: Put the mixers away dirty. In the morning, tell the store manager what Kathy did.

    Possible results: _____

    _____

3. Choice C: Stay and clean the mixers yourself.

    Possible results: _____

    _____

4. Choice D: Try to convince Kathy to stay and help clean the mixers.

    Possible results: _____

    _____

5. Now explain which choice you think will have the best results, or suggest another choice:

    _____

Exercise 3 Analysis

Analyzing a Decision

Name _____ Date _____

Think of someone who you think has made a wise decision recently. This might be someone you know. It could also be someone you have read or heard about. It might be a relative, a neighbor, or a friend. If you have trouble thinking of someone, look in a newspaper or magazine for ideas.

Once you have thought about this person's decision, answer the questions below. Do not write anything that might embarrass someone. Don't share any information you don't think other people should know or discuss.

1. What decision did this person make?

   _____

   _____

   _____

2. What were some other choices the person could have made?

   _____

   _____

   _____

3. Many people think these six qualities are important: honesty, responsibility, courage, concern and respect for others, good health, and good citizenship. Which of these qualities do you think guided this person's decision? Why?

   _____

   _____

   _____

4. Why do you think this person's decision was wise?

   _____

   _____

   _____

Exercise 4   Application   Recognizing Responsibility

Name _____ Date _____

With a partner, read the situations below. Write an excuse someone might use to avoid taking responsibility for the action. Then write a responsible action for each one. The first one is done for you. Share your answers with your partner.

1. Shelly lost Kara's sweater. Now Kara is angry.

    a. An excuse Shelly might give:

    Shelly tells Kara, "You never should have lent me that sweater if it was so

    important to you."

    b. A responsible action Shelly could take:

    Shelly buys Kara a new sweater.

2. Kamal didn't make the track team.

    a. An excuse Kamal might give:

    _____

    _____

    b. A responsible action he could take:

    _____

    _____

3. Jeff was supposed to start dinner when he got home from school. He forgot to do it, and his parents are angry.

    a. An excuse Jeff might give:

    _____

    _____

    b. A responsible action he might take:

    _____

    _____

Exercise 5 Analysis   Setting Priorities

Name _____ Date _____

Read the information below. Then fill in the chart to help Evan set his priorities. Help him put his goals in order from most important to least.

Evan has so much going on in his life that he can't sort it all out. For example:

- He likes to play the piano and wants to take lessons so he can play better.
- He has a good chance of getting a scholarship at the local community college. However, Evan is having trouble with his grade in social studies. To get the scholarship, he must bring his social studies grade up to at least a B.
- A new girl sits next to him in homeroom, and he would like to get to know her better.
- Evan wants to get a job so he can buy a used car some day.

1.

Priority	Goal
1	
2	
3	
4	

2. Compare charts with a partner. Discuss the way that you and your partner ordered Evan's goals. Were they the same? Why or why not?

_____

_____

_____

_____

Exercise 6 Evaluation   Reaching Goals

Name _____ Date _____

Carmen is determined to get a part in the school play. Read the paragraphs below and help Carmen figure out what else she could do to reach her goal.

Carmen has read the whole play several times. She has also chosen the character she would like to play.

Every evening, Carmen spends an hour in her room reading her character's lines in the play. She knows that her soft voice might keep her from getting the part, so she is practicing speaking loudly. She has carefully marked the date of the tryouts on her calendar. However, Carmen knows several other people will be trying out for the same part. She's still worried she might not get the part.

Read over the steps in reaching a goal. Then explain which step or steps Carmen has overlooked. What else could she have done to increase her chances of reaching her goal?

Step 1: Write down Carmen's goal.

Step 2: List steps to reach the goal.

Step 3: Set up a timeline.

Step 4: Identify any obstacles.

Step 5: Identify sources of help.

Step 6: Check your progress.

_____

_____

_____

_____

_____

_____

_____

Exercise 7   Analysis   **Managing Time**

Name _____ Date _____

Answer the questions below.

1. With a partner, read these quotations about time. Circle the quotation that you both like best.

    - It takes time to save time. *Joe Taylor*

    - Every minute starts an hour. *Paul Gondola*

    - One of these days is none of these days. *English proverb*

    - What may be done at any time will be done at no time. *Scottish proverb*

    - You will never "find" time for anything. If you want time, you must make it. *Charles Buxton*

2. Answer the questions below using the quotation you circled.

    a. What do you think the quotation means?

    _____

    _____

    _____

    b. Why do you like this quotation?

    _____

    _____

    _____

    c. How might this quotation help people manage their time?

    _____

    _____

    _____

Share your answers with your classmates.

Exercise 8   Synthesis   Identifying Time Wasters

Name _____ Date _____

Think about the ways that you waste time. Choose your biggest time waster. Then follow the steps below to write an action plan that will help you stop wasting time.

Step 1: Write down your goal. Describe the time waster you will eliminate.

_____

_____

Step 2: List steps to reach the goal.

_____

_____

Step 3: Set up a timeline.

_____

_____

Step 4: Identify any obstacles in reaching your goal.

_____

_____

Step 5: Identify sources of help.

_____

_____

Step 6: Explain how you will check your progress.

_____

_____

Exercise 9   Evaluation   Identifying Friends

Name _____ Date _____

Read the situation below. As you read, think about whether Stephan is a good friend for Albie or for Marguerite.

Stephan, Marguerite, and Albie were talking in the school hallway one afternoon.

"Albie, you're usually a lot more fun," Stephan said. "If you were really my friend, you'd come to my party tonight."

Albie shrugged his shoulders. "I don't enjoy parties like that, so I'm not going."

"Well, I'm counting on you to show up, Albie. You, too, Marguerite." With that, Stephan walked away.

"Why don't you like Stephan's parties, Albie?" Marguerite asked.

"Well, for one thing, Stephan told me his parents aren't going to be home. I bet they don't even know he's having a party," Albie said. "The last time Stephan had a party, his neighbors called the police. I don't want to be there when that happens."

"I've never been to one of Stephan's parties," Marguerite said, "but I think I should go. I'll tell you all about it on Monday."

Answer the following questions.

1. Is Stephan a good friend for Albie? Why or why not?

   _____

   _____

   _____

2. Is Stephan a good friend for Marguerite? Why or why not?

   _____

   _____

   _____

3. Are Albie and Marguerite good friends for Stephan? Why or why not?

   _____

   _____

   _____

   _____

Exercise 10 Analysis   **Resisting Peer Pressure**

Name _____ Date _____

Ian, Kun-Pei, and Kevin all go to East High School. Read their descriptions below. Then work with a partner to answer the questions.

Ian	Ian is new at school this year. He spends most of his time after school watching MTV. He always tries to dress and act the same way the people do on the MTV shows.
Kun-Pei	Kun-Pei has three good friends, and they like art as much as she does. They are taking a painting class together. Every month, the four of them go to the museum downtown to see the new exhibits.
Kevin	Kevin is on the basketball team and works part-time. He hopes to get a basketball scholarship so he can go to the community college. He's also saving what he earns from his job to pay for tuition and books. He won't let anything get in the way of winning that scholarship and going to college.

Nose rings are a new fad at East High. Discuss the following questions with your partner. Write what you decide. Explain your decision.

1. Do you think Ian would get a nose ring? Why or why not?

   _____

   _____

   _____

2. Do you think Kun-Pei would get a nose ring? Why or why not?

   _____

   _____

   _____

3. Do you think Kevin would get a nose ring? Why or why not?

   _____

   _____

   _____

Exercise 11   Evaluation   Saying "No"

Name _____ Date _____

Read the situation below. Then answer the questions that follow.

BJ, Judi, Maya, and Earl had just finished lunch in the school cafeteria. BJ opened his bookbag so the others could see a pack of cigarettes he had hidden in there. "I need a cigarette. Let's go smoke out behind the gym," he said.

Judi started stuffing her things in her bag. She didn't look at BJ as she said, "Not today. Maybe tomorrow."

Maya looked calmly at BJ and shook her head. She said, "I don't smoke."

Earl shoved his chair back and stood up. "Are you kidding, BJ?" he shouted. "Do you want to get me thrown off the football team? You're nuts! I'm out of here."

1. Which friend is BJ likely to keep pressuring? Why? What could this person have said or done differently so BJ would not keep up his pressure?

   _____

   _____

   _____

   _____

2. Which friend put too much energy in his or her refusal? What problems could this cause? What should this person have said or done differently?

   _____

   _____

   _____

   _____

3. Which friend's refusal was best? What made it the best?

   _____

   _____

   _____

   _____

Exercise 12 Synthesis   Understanding Yourself

Name _____ Date _____

Read the situation below. Then work with a partner to answer the questions.

When Anna got to a friend's party, she walked into the kitchen. She was surprised to see a keg of beer there. Some teenagers in the kitchen were holding cups of beer and laughing together. Anna didn't really like the taste of beer, but she poured herself a cup.

Tyrone got to the party a little later. He also walked into the kitchen. He saw the keg of beer and noticed some people drinking it. He looked around until he found some soft drinks in a cooler. He took a can and went into the living room to see who else was there.

1. Anna doesn't like beer, but she still poured herself some.

   a. What do you think Anna told herself?

   _____

   _____

   _____

   b. Was she being honest with herself? Explain your answer.

   _____

   _____

   _____

2. Tyrone saw other kids drinking, but he ignored the beer.

   a. What do you think Tyrone told himself?

   _____

   _____

   _____

   b. Was he being honest with himself? Explain your answer.

   _____

   _____

   _____

Exercise 13   Analysis   Checking Listening Skills

Name _____ Date _____

Lee thinks he's a good listener. Read the conversation below and see what you think. Decide whether his words and actions show that he's listening to Bernadette.

Bernadette: "Our oral book reports are due tomorrow, and I'm worried."

Lee: "I haven't even picked a book yet!"

1. Is this good listening? Explain your answer.

_____

_____

_____

_____

Bernadette: "I'm worried that I'm going to forget what I wanted to say."

Lee: (watching someone come into the room) "You should use note cards. That's what I do."

2. Is this good listening? Explain your answer.

_____

_____

_____

_____

Bernadette: "I always feel like everyone is passing notes while I'm talking."

Lee: (nodding) "Does that bother you?"

3. Is this good listening? Explain your answer.

_____

_____

_____

_____

Exercise 14 Analysis   Rating Yourself

Name _____ Date _____

To find out what kind of listener you are, fill in the chart below. First, read each good listening skill. Then place a check in the column that tells how often you use that skill.

Good Listening Skills	Often	Sometimes	Never
I pay attention to the person speaking and don't look around the room.			
I let the person talk and don't interrupt.			
I ask questions about what the person is saying.			
I listen for what the person is feeling.			
I summarize what the person said in my own words.			

Now look over your completed chart and set a listening goal.

a. Which good listening skill will you try to use more often? Why?

_____

_____

_____

b. How will you remember to use this skill more often?

_____

_____

_____

c. Why is it important to use this skill?

_____

_____

_____

Exercise 15 Evaluation   Understanding Body Language

Name _____ Date _____

Look at each photo below and read what the person is saying.

"I don't believe it—that can't be true."   "No, I'm ok. I'm not upset."

1. Does the person on the left mean what she is saying? Explain your answer.

_____

_____

_____

_____

_____

2. Does the person on the right mean what he is saying? Explain your answer.

_____

_____

_____

_____

_____

_____

Exercise 16   Application   Putting Skills to Work

Name _____ Date _____

Rose needs a good listener. Read what she has to say below. Explain what you would do and say to be a good listener.

Rose tells you, "I cheated on a science test at school. I know it was wrong."

1. Write what you would do to show you are listening.

    _____

    _____

    _____

    _____

    _____

    _____

2. Write some things you might say to show you are listening.

    _____

    _____

    _____

    _____

    _____

3. Now write something you would *not* say to Rose. Then explain why you would not say it.

    _____

    _____

    _____

    _____

Exercise 17 Application   Recognizing Other Points of View

Name _____ Date _____

Read each point of view below. Then think of the other person's point of view in the same situation. Explain your answer to a partner and see if your answers are the same.

1. Ingrid thinks that Liam is being bossy. He wants to do their science report on crystals, and he won't even listen to her ideas.

   a. Write Liam's possible point of view. _____

   _____

   _____

   b. Write Ingrid's possible point of view. _____

   _____

   _____

2. Ahmad thinks Raina is being disrespectful. She was supposed to meet him at the movie theater at 8:00 P.M. It's already 8:15, and she's nowhere in sight.

   a. Write Raina's possible point of view. _____

   _____

   _____

   b. Write Ahmad's possible point of view. _____

   _____

   _____

3. Jordan thinks that anyone who chooses to live in a noisy, crowded city must be crazy.

   Write another possible point of view.

   _____

   _____

   _____

Exercise 18   Application   Using "I Messages"

Name _____ Date _____

Read the angry responses below. For each one, work with a partner to write an "I message" that explains the person's feelings.

The parts of an "I message":

I feel . . . (name how you feel, such as angry, embarrassed, or worried)
when you . . . (explain what is bothering you)
because . . . (tell why this bothers you)

1. "I will never, ever let you borrow any of my clothes again! You always lose everything!"

   Your "I message":

   _____

   _____

   _____

   _____

2. "You always laugh when I tell you my feelings. I'm never telling you another thing!"

   Your "I message":

   _____

   _____

   _____

3. To a brother or sister: "You are a lazy slob! Why don't you ever clean up your own dishes?"

   His or her "I message":

   _____

   _____

   _____

Exercise 19 Analysis   **Recognizing Respect in Others**

Name _____ Date _____

Chandra, Hannah, and Amy are trying to decide which movie to see. Read their conversation below. Then work with a group to discuss and answer the questions.

"Anything you want to see is okay with me," Chandra told her friends.

"But you kept yawning in that action movie we saw last week," Hannah pointed out. "You don't want to see another action movie, do you?"

Chandra shrugged her shoulders. "I don't care."

"Well, I know what I want to see." Amy pointed to an ad in the newspaper. "This is the best movie out now. It has my favorite actors and lots of action." She checked her watch. "It starts in half an hour, so let's get moving. I don't want to miss any of it."

1. Does Hannah respect Chandra? How can you tell?

_____

_____

_____

2. Does Amy respect Chandra? How can you tell?

_____

_____

_____

3. Does Chandra respect herself? How can you tell?

_____

_____

_____

4. Whom does Amy respect? How can you tell? How could she be more respectful?

_____

_____

_____

_____

Exercise 20   Synthesis   Dealing with Anger

Name _____ Date _____

Ira and Ruben are arguing in the locker room. Their team just lost an important basketball game. Read their conversation below. Then answer the questions that follow.

"Why didn't you pass the ball to me?" Ira shouts at Ruben. "I was right under the basket! But you had to take the shot yourself and miss! You cost us that game!"

"I thought I could make three points from where I was!" Ruben shouts back. "Anyway, you missed two foul shots in the third quarter, Ira. If you were a better shot, we would have won that game!"

1. Ruben and Ira are both angry. What are two things that could be making them angry?

   _____

   _____

   _____

   _____

   _____

2. What are some ways that Ira and Ruben can calm their angry feelings?

   _____

   _____

   _____

   _____

   _____

3. What could they have said to help each other feel better about losing the game?

   _____

   _____

   _____

   _____

   _____

Exercise 21 Evaluation   Settling Conflicts

Name _____ Date _____

Read the situation below. Then answer the questions.

Maria and Keith both have to do a report on ants for biology class. Their reports are due on Monday. Maria has already been to the library and taken out the only books on ants. Keith could not find any other information for his report.

Keith says, "Maria, I need those books, too. Maybe we could get together this weekend. Then we could both use them."

Maria shakes her head. "That won't work. My family is going to my grandmother's for the weekend, and I'm taking the books with me. Sorry."

1. Is this conflict settled? Why or why not?

_____

_____

_____

_____

_____

2. How did Keith try to settle the conflict?

_____

_____

_____

_____

3. What else might Maria and Keith do to settle their conflict?

_____

_____

_____

_____

_____

Exercise 22 Synthesis   Coping with Change

Name _____ Date _____

During a person's teenage years, it can be difficult to handle all the changes that occur. Work with a group to fill in the chart below. Add as many changes and responses as you can. In the response box, write what you might say, feel, or do because of the change. Then share your ideas with the rest of the class. Be sure not to discuss anything that might embarrass someone. The first row shows one example.

Type of Change	A Teenager's Best Response
Physical Changes Growing taller	Accept your height. It might still be changing. Millions of people are as short—or as tall—as you.
Emotional Changes	
Social Changes	
Mental Changes	

Exercise 23   Synthesis   Conducting an Interview

Name _____ Date _____

Work with a group to find out how other people handled change during their teenage years. Each group member should interview one person who is 20 years old or older. This person should be someone you are comfortable with. Try a family member, neighbor, teacher, coach, or friend.

Ask the questions below, plus any others that you think are important. Avoid any questions that might embarrass the person you're interviewing.

1. What kinds of changes happened to you during your teenage years?

   _____

   _____

2. How did you feel about these changes?

   _____

   _____

3. What helped you deal with these changes?

   _____

   _____

4. What advice do you have for young people who are experiencing these changes now?

   _____

   _____

After everyone has completed an interview, discuss with your group what you learned. Then list two or three things the group found out about teenage changes. Share these findings with the rest of the class.

5. Here is what my group learned from our interviews.

   _____

   _____

   _____

Exercise 24   Synthesis   Writing a Letter of Advice

Name _____ Date _____

Families face many changes over the years. They might experience changes in the people who belong to the family or the people who live in the home. Families might also have to deal with a member's illness, a change in income, or a move to another city or state.

To think about family changes, follow the steps below.

1. With a partner, create an imaginary family that includes a teenager. Describe the family members and their ages below. Include all the information you think is important about the family. For example, decide where they live and work.

    _____

    _____

    _____

    _____

2. Think of a way this family might change. Describe the change.

    _____

    _____

    _____

    _____

3. Write a letter to the teenager in the family. Suggest ways to deal with this kind of family change.

    Dear _____ ,

    _____

    _____

    _____

    _____

    _____

    _____

Exercise 25   Application   Creating a Poster

Name _____ Date _____

Think of a common cause of stress for the students at your school. Then design a poster that explains two or more ways that might help them deal with stress. Make your poster clear, helpful, and colorful. Suggest ways to deal with stress that are practical for high school students. Use the space below to draw the poster.

Make sure your poster does not contain anything that might embarrass students, teachers, or visitors to your school.

Exercise 26   Analysis   Identifying Changes in the Community

Name _____ Date _____

Work with a partner and look through your newspaper for several days. Watch for articles that show how your community is changing. Copy or paste the headlines in the box below.

```
┌─────────────────────────────────────────────────────────────────────┐
│                                                                     │
│                                                                     │
│                                                                     │
│                                                                     │
│                                                                     │
│                                                                     │
│                                                                     │
│                                                                     │
│                                                                     │
└─────────────────────────────────────────────────────────────────────┘
```

Now read over your collection of articles. Work with your partner to fill in this chart.

Type of Change in the Community	Ways the Change Affects Your Family	Is the Change Positive or Negative?
1.		
2.		
3.		
4.		
5.		

Exercise 27   Application   Using the Food Guide Pyramid

Name _____ Date _____

Work with a partner to plan a balanced diet for one day. Fill in the chart below.

Meal	Kinds of Food	Number of Servings
Breakfast		____ Fats, Oils, Sweets ____ Milk, Cheese, Yogurt ____ Meat, Chicken, Eggs, Fish ____ Fruits, Vegetables ____ Bread, Cereal, Rice, Pasta
Lunch		____ Fats, Oils, Sweets ____ Milk, Cheese, Yogurt ____ Meat, Chicken, Eggs, Fish ____ Fruits, Vegetables ____ Bread, Cereal, Rice, Pasta
Dinner		____ Fats, Oils, Sweets ____ Milk, Cheese, Yogurt ____ Meat, Chicken, Eggs, Fish ____ Fruits, Vegetables ____ Bread, Cereal, Rice, Pasta
Snacks		____ Fats, Oils, Sweets ____ Milk, Cheese, Yogurt ____ Meat, Chicken, Eggs, Fish ____ Fruits, Vegetables ____ Bread, Cereal, Rice, Pasta

Now add the total number of servings for the day you planned.

_____ Fats, Oils, Sweets   _____ Meat, Chicken, Eggs, Fish

_____ Milk, Cheese, Yogurt   _____ Fruits and Vegetables   _____ Bread, Cereal, Rice, Pasta

Compare the number of servings in your plan with the number of servings suggested in the Food Guide Pyramid. What changes should you make in your plan?

_____

_____

Exercise 28 Evaluation   Evaluating Fitness Programs

Name _____ Date _____

Josh thinks he gets enough exercise to stay fit. Read the paragraphs below and decide for yourself.

Josh studies several evenings a week in his bedroom. During the evening, he reads and works on his computer.

At least once every hour, Josh exercises by running downstairs to the kitchen. He usually goes down to get a snack, such as fruit or a bagel. Other times, he runs downstairs to phone his friends and find out what they're doing. Then he runs back upstairs to his room.

1. Does running up and down one set of stairs make your heart work harder? Why or why not?

   _____

   _____

   _____

   _____

   _____

2. Is running up and down one set of stairs once an hour aerobic exercise? Why or why not?

   _____

   _____

   _____

   _____

   _____

3. If this is Josh's whole exercise program, will he stay fit? Why or why not?

   _____

   _____

   _____

   _____

Exercise 29   Synthesis   Writing a Letter of Advice

Name _____ Date _____

You have learned ways to deal with peer pressure. You have also learned more about what happens when someone starts smoking. Read the situation below and write a letter to your cousin. Help him or her resist the pressure to start smoking.

Imagine you have a cousin who is in the sixth grade and lives in another state. Your cousin looks up to you because you are older.

Today you got a letter from your cousin. His or her best friend has started to smoke. The friend is pressuring your cousin to start smoking. Your cousin doesn't know what to do.

First, write down some points you want to include in your letter. Then write your letter.

1. Points I want to include:

    _____

    _____

    _____

    _____

2. Dear Cousin,

    _____

    _____

    _____

    _____

    _____

    _____

    _____

    _____

    _____

    _____

Exercise 30 Analysis   **Recognizing Dangerous Situations**

Name _____ Date _____

Work with a group to list places near your school or in your community where a young person alone might be in danger. For example, maybe the neighborhood includes empty buildings. Maybe big trees block the light from streetlights. Maybe people who cause trouble tend to gather at a certain store or mall.

Share your group's list with the class. Then discuss these questions as a class.

1. Did several groups list the same places? If so, what does this tell you?

   _____

   _____

   _____

2. What do the places listed have in common?

   _____

   _____

   _____

3. Did only one group list a certain place? Why might that happen?

   _____

   _____

   _____

4. Will today's discussion change where you go in the community or whether you go out alone? If so, how?

   _____

   _____

   _____

5. What might be done to make any dangerous places in your community safer for everyone?

   _____

   _____

   _____

Exercise 31   Analysis   Understanding Types of Doctors

Name _____ Date _____

Doctors are listed under various headings in the Yellow Pages of the phone book. To find the right kind of doctor, you need to understand what the headings mean.

1. Read these word parts and their definitions.

dermo-	relating to skin
obste-	relating to childbirth
ophthalmo-	relating to eyes
ortho-	relating to bones
pedia-	relating to children
podia-	relating to feet
psych-	relating to thinking

2. Now read each problem below. On the line, write the kind of doctor each person would want to see.

pediatrician	ophthalmologist	obstetrician
podiatrist	orthopedist	dermatologist
psychiatrist		

a. Loretta has a mysterious rash. _____

b. David's feet hurt when he walks. _____

c. In the emergency room at the hospital, Keisha learns that her knee is broken.

_____

d. Martin feels depressed. _____

e. Maria's baby brother has a high fever. _____

f. John has trouble reading small type. _____

g. Susan's older sister is pregnant. _____

Exercise 32   Evaluation   Making Decisions about Medicine

Name _____ Date _____

Lana thinks she is doing Benjamin a favor. Read the situation below and see if you agree. Then answer the questions.

Lana and Benjamin were walking home from school. Benjamin kept walking slower and slower. "I feel terrible," he moaned. "My throat is killing me."

"I had a sore throat just last week," Lana said. "When I went to the doctor, he gave me a prescription for some pills. I have some left. When we get to my house, I'll give them to you. They really helped me a lot. I feel fine now."

"Are you sure I should take them?" Benjamin asked. "I'm already taking some medicine my mom gave me."

"Sure! It says right on the label how many pills to take and how often to take them," Lana told him.

1. Should Benjamin take Lana's pills? Why or why not?

   _____

   _____

   _____

   _____

2. Do the directions on the label mean that anyone can take that medicine? Why or why not?

   _____

   _____

   _____

   _____

3. What should Benjamin do if he's feeling sick?

   _____

   _____

   _____

   _____

Exercise 33   Analysis

Analyzing Insurance

Name _____ Date _____

Choosing an insurance plan can be a difficult decision. With a partner, read about Plan A and Plan B. Then list some advantages and disadvantages for each plan. Decide which plan you would choose.

	Plan A	Plan B
Costs	$75 per month	$50 per month
Doctors	Chosen by insurance company	Any doctor you choose
Covered costs for doctor visits and hospital	Covers 100% of doctor visits, including physicals. No charge for hospital stay if you go to a hospital selected by the insurance company.	You pay first $200 per year of any medical expense. Then insurance pays 80% of all other costs.
Prescriptions	$10 for all prescriptions	$10 for all prescriptions

1. *Plan A*

   a. Advantages: _____

   _____

   b. Disadvantages: _____

   _____

2. *Plan B*

   a. Advantages: _____

   _____

   b. Disadvantages: _____

   _____

3. Which plan would you choose? Why? _____

   _____

   _____

   _____

Exercise 34   Analysis   Rating Risks

Name _____ Date _____

With a group, discuss this list of risks in the home. Add other in-home risks to the list, if you wish. Decide which of the risks teenagers are most likely to face. Then put the risks in order, starting with the highest risk for teenagers.

Share your rating with the other groups. Discuss any differences in the way the groups rated the risks.

Possible Risks

burns from fire	falls	broken bones
poisoning	cuts	head wounds
electrical shock	falling objects	slipping

Our Group's Decision

1. Highest risk for teenagers: _____

   _____

   _____

   _____

   _____

2. Lowest risk for teenagers: _____

3. Below, explain why you put the risks in this order.

   _____

   _____

   _____

   _____

   _____

   _____

Exercise 35 Application   Planning for an Emergency

Name _____ Date _____

Do you have a plan for emergencies at home? In the box below, draw the rooms in your home. Use both boxes if your home has two floors. From each room, draw a green arrow to the exit you would use in case of fire. Then from each room, draw a yellow arrow to an exit you could use if the first exit is blocked.

Downstairs

Upstairs

Exercise 36 Application

Handling an Emergency

Name _____ Date _____

Handling an emergency in your home can be difficult. However, dealing with an emergency while you are in someone else's home can be even harder. With a partner, read the situation below. Then answer the questions. Share your answers with the class.

Kyle was baby-sitting for 2-year-old Jeremy for the second time. At 8:00, he put Jeremy to bed for the night. Then he went into the living room to watch basketball on TV.

Half an hour later, Jeremy wandered into the living room. He had some kind of white powder around his mouth. Kyle tried to get Jeremy to tell him what it was, but Jeremy began to cry.

Kyle quickly searched the house and found an open cabinet under a bathroom sink. He saw several containers of powder knocked over, including baby powder and scouring powder.

1. Kyle knows he needs help. What should he do?

_____

_____

_____

_____

2. What are some things that could have been done to avoid this emergency?

_____

_____

_____

3. How might you handle this emergency?

_____

_____

_____

_____

Exercise 37   Analysis   Identifying Qualities

Name _____ Date _____

List three personal qualities that you think would be important for each job below. Here are some examples of personal qualities: careful, outgoing, fair, and independent. You may think of many other qualities to put on your lists.

1.

Job	Necessary Personal Qualities
Bank Teller	a. _____ b. _____ c. _____
Emergency Medical Technician (EMT)	a. _____ b. _____ c. _____
Welder	a. _____ b. _____ c. _____

Now listen carefully as several students read their lists of qualities to the class. Then discuss these questions and why they might be important.

2. Which qualities were named most often for each of these jobs?

a. Bank Teller: _____

b. EMT: _____

c. Welder: _____

3. How could you find out which qualities are actually needed for a certain job?

    _____

4. Why is it important to learn which personal qualities are necessary for a job?

    _____

    _____

Exercise 38 Analysis   Using Want Ads

Name _____ Date _____

Complete the exercises below.

1. Work with a partner to find newspaper help-wanted ads that have abbreviations. Cut them out and paste them in the space below.

2. Write each abbreviation and its meaning below.

Abbreviation	Meaning

3. Now choose one of your ads. Pretend that you are going to call and ask about the job. Write two questions you would ask that are not answered in the ad. Your questions might help you decide whether you want the job or whether you are qualified for the job.

a. _____

    _____

b. _____

    _____

Exercise 39   Application   Matching Jobs and People

Name _____ Date _____

**Look through the want ads below. Then find a job for each person.
Explain why you chose that job.**

| HELP WANTED 2156 | Expert repair person M/F. Minimum 15 years experience. Excellent wages. Company truck. Call 555-2113 | Salesperson needed for weekends and evenings. Apply in person at Unfinished Wood Prod. 4769 Sawmill Rd. |

STEVE STEAMER CLEANERS

MANHATTAN BAGEL SHOP

Carpet cleaning technicians.
Training and career oppor. Latest equipment and van. Benefits, ins. Call Steve Steamer, 555-1860

Customer Service. No evening hours. Manhattan Bagel shop needs friendly people to help our customers. Flexible hrs/oppor. for advancement. Call 555-2989

PT office help needed for apartment community. Must be well organized and flexible. Call 555-5813

Nurse's Aide
Certificate not necessary. Needed for all shifts in assisted-living facility. Call 555-5823

1. Wanda is outgoing and has a daughter in first grade. She is taking business courses at the community college during the day.

    She should apply for the job of _____

    because _____

    _____

2. Hank would like to have his own business someday, but he's not sure what it would be. He likes to work with his hands.

    He should apply for the job of _____

    because _____

    _____

3. Cindy is taking courses so she can become a licensed practical nurse (LPN). She knows she will have a lot of competition when she is ready to apply for a job as an LPN.

    She should apply for the job of _____

    because _____

    _____

Exercise 40   Synthesis

Writing a Letter of Advice

Name _____ Date _____

Pretend that a friend will graduate soon. This friend wants to get a job but doesn't know which one would be best. Your friend lives in another state, so you must write to him or her.

In your letter, tell your friend how to identify the right job. Name some ways to find out more about jobs that seem interesting. Explain how to figure out which jobs are available in the community.

Dear _____ ,

_____

_____

_____

_____

_____

_____

_____

_____

_____

_____

_____

_____

_____

_____

_____

_____

_____

Exercise 41   Application   Writing a Résumé

Name _____ Date _____

To write your own résumé, begin by filling in the information below. Then type your résumé on another sheet of paper. Leave out the directions that are in parentheses ( ).

(your name) _____

(your complete address) _____

(your phone number) _____

Job Objective (the kind of job you want) _____

Education (the names of the schools you have attended and the year you graduated or will graduate from each one)

_____

(any special courses or training you have had) _____

Experience

_____   (company name) _____

(the date you started   (your job title) _____
the job you have now)
                                 (your job responsibilities; include details that show
                                 you are doing a good job and are a trusted employee)

                                 _____

                                 _____

                                 _____

_____   (company name) _____

(the dates you started &   (your job title) _____
ended your earlier job)
                                 (your job responsibilities) _____

                                 _____

                                 _____

(Describe the other jobs you have had in the same way as you did above.)

Skills (skills, interests, honors, or awards that relate to this job)

_____

_____

Exercise 42   Application   Describing Yourself

Name _____ Date _____

Think of a job you might like to apply for. Then fill in the job application below.

APPLICATION FOR EMPLOYMENT

Date _____

Personal Information

Name _____ Social Security Number _____

Address _____
         Street   City   State   Zip

Number of years at this address _____ Phone _____

Are you 18 years of age or older? yes _____ no _____

Job you are applying for _____ Hourly pay expected _____

Do you have any physical handicaps or disabilities that would prevent you from doing this job? _____ If so, please describe the disability and how it affects you.

_____

Date when you can start working _____

Education

	Name and address	Number of years there	Graduated: yes/no	Course or major
High school				
College				
Graduate school				
Trade school				

Military Service   Served in U.S. Armed Forces? yes _____ no _____ Branch of service _____

Work Experience

Company name and address	Dates of employment	Supervisor's name	Job title	Salary	Reason for leaving

References

Name and Occupation	Address	Phone	Years acquainted

I certify that the information I have provided is true. I understand that if you find any deliberate errors, I will not be considered for employment.

_____   _____
Signature   Date

Exercise 43   Synthesis   Building Interviewing Skills

Name _____ Date _____

Ron is interviewing for a job as a salesperson in a clothing store. Read his interview below. Then imagine you are the person being interviewed. Rewrite the interview in a way that might help you get the same job.

Interviewer: Tell me about yourself.

Ron: Well, I'm 17 and I go to North High. My parents' names are Jeff and Carla, but they're divorced now. I have a younger brother and an older sister.

Interviewer: I see. Why do you want to work for this store?

Ron: It doesn't matter where I work. I just want a job.

Interviewer: Our salespeople stock the shelves and keep them neat. How do you feel about that?

Ron: I'll do it if I have to, but I'd rather just sell stuff.

Interviewer: Well, thank you for coming in, Ron. We'll call you by Friday if we choose you for the job.

Your Interview

Interviewer: Tell me about yourself.

You: _____

_____

Interviewer: Why do you want to work for this store?

You: _____

_____

Interviewer: Our salespeople stock the shelves and keep them neat. How do you feel about that?

You: _____

_____

Exercise 44   Analysis   Choosing between Jobs

Name _____ Date _____

Read about Annette and her two job choices. Next, explain why she might and might not like each job. Then recommend the job you think she should take.

Annette will graduate from high school next month. She is shy but gets over this after a while. She is patient and good at taking care of details. Her favorite courses in high school are math and data processing. Annette likes to hike and camp with her friends and family.

Bank Teller   Annette would begin this job by spending a month at four different bank offices. She would help people cash checks and make deposits. Tellers must firmly ask for identification each time someone wants to cash a check. The job pays $6.50 an hour. After her training, Annette would work at an office that is a 10-minute bus ride from her home.

1. Why Annette might like this job: _____

   _____

2. Why she might not like this job: _____

   _____

Surveyor   This job at an engineering company involves mapping out roads. Annette would work on a team measuring distances. Then the team would use its meaurements to draw maps. The job pays $6 an hour and is a 30-minute bus ride from Annette's home.

3. Why Annette might like this job: _____

   _____

4. Why she might not like this job: _____

   _____

5. Here's the job I recommend for Annette and the reasons I recommend it:

   _____

   _____

Exercise 45   Application   Creating a Handbook

Name _____ Date _____

Right now, your main job is going to school. Like most companies, most schools have handbooks that describe the way things work. If your school has a student handbook, don't look through it until you have finished this activity.

Employee or student handbooks begin with a table of contents. This page lists the topics covered in the handbook. For example, an employee handbook might list the company's departments and what they each do. It probably lists company rules. It might also list job benefits.

Work with one or two partners to create a table of contents for a student handbook at your school. Think about what students at your school need to know. Then list the topics that should be included in the student handbook. Use another sheet of paper if you need more space.

The first example is done for you.

**School Handbook
Table of Contents**

1. Student Dress Code _____

    A. Clothes that can be worn by students in school. _____

    B. Clothes that cannot be worn by students in school. _____

2. _____

    A. _____

    B. _____

3. _____

    A. _____

    B. _____

4. _____

    A. _____

    B. _____

Exercise 46 Evaluation   Identifying Responsible Behavior

Name _____ Date _____

Being responsible is very important for keeping a job. But it's difficult to know what actions are responsible. With a group, read the situations below. Then write a responsible answer for each one.

1. You work in the locker room of a swimming pool. The pool provides free towels for swimmers. One man thinks there is a one dollar charge for the towel. He speaks a language you do not understand. Your coworker whispers, "Take his money and keep it. That's what I do." The man keeps handing you his dollar.

    a. Your group recommends: _____

    _____

    _____

    _____

    b. The reasons for your recommendation: _____

    _____

    _____

    _____

2. Where you work, employees must sign in and out. One morning your coworker calls you from home. She overslept and wants you to sign in for her. It will take her an hour to get to work, but she doesn't want her boss to know she isn't there.

    a. Your group recommends: _____

    _____

    _____

    _____

    b. The reasons for your recommendation: _____

    _____

    _____

    _____

Exercise 47 Application

Working with Customers

Name _____ Date _____

A teenager named Jack just started his new job at a dry cleaning shop. He helps customers who bring in clothing to be cleaned. Read the conversation below and answer the questions about it.

Jack:	What do you want?
Customer:	I have some shirts to be dry cleaned. There are three. No, maybe I have four of them.
Jack:	Well, which is it?
Customer:	Four, I guess.
Jack:	Maybe I better count them myself.
Customer:	Never mind. I'll take them to another dry cleaner.

1. Why do you think the customer decided to go to another dry cleaner?

   _____

   _____

   _____

2. Imagine you have Jack's job. Rewrite the conversation above, showing how you would treat the customer with more respect.

   You: _____

   _____

   Customer: I have some shirts to be dry cleaned. There are three. No, maybe I have four of them.

   You: _____

   _____

   Customer: I'd like them with not too much starch and on hangers.

   You: _____

   _____

   Customer: _____

Exercise 48 Synthesis   Conducting an Interview

Name _____ Date _____

Find out if employees need to learn new skills on their jobs. Interview some-one who has had the same job for at least one year. You might interview a family member, a neighbor, or a friend. Ask the person you interview the questions below.

1. What is your job and how long have you had it?

    _____

2. What new skills have you learned since you started this job?

    _____

    _____

    _____

3. Have you attended any courses, training sessions, or classes related to this job? If so, what did you learn?

    _____

    _____

    _____

4. How have these new skills and knowledge helped you on your job?

    _____

    _____

    _____

After your interview, discuss what you learned with a group of classmates. Then answer the questions below.

5. Does every employee need to learn new skills on the job? Why or why not?

    _____

    _____

    _____

Exercise 49 Evaluation

Looking at Teamwork

Name _____ Date _____

Read the following situations. Then answer the questions.

1. Colleen and Katie both work in a snack shop. Colleen likes to cook, so she prepares the salads and sandwiches. Katie likes to talk to people, so she takes the customers' orders and keeps the front counter and tables clean.

   Are Colleen and Katie working as a team? Why or why not?

   _____

   _____

   _____

2. Greg and James have started a lawn-mowing service. They each paid half of the cost of a lawn mower. They put up flyers and asked customers to call the phone number at Greg's house. Greg says he can't mow any lawns. He has to stay home so he can answer the phone and schedule the customers. James mows all the lawns. Greg takes half of the money they make and gives the other half to James. Greg uses some of his money to go out with his friends in the evening. James is too tired to go out.

   Are Greg and James working as a team? Why or why not?

   _____

   _____

   _____

3. Brenda and Aaron work at a computer factory. They glue in the computer parts. Several times a day, Aaron finds mistakes in the way Brenda glues in a part. "So what?" Brenda says. "If the computer doesn't work, the customer will just bring it back and get another one!" Aaron often tries to fix her mistakes so the computers will work correctly.

   Are Brenda and Aaron working as a team? Why or why not?

   _____

   _____

   _____

Exercise 50   Synthesis   Charting a Career Path

Name _____ Date _____

Emily wants to have her own clothing shop someday. She will be graduating from high school in two years.

Write the steps Emily could take to meet her goal. Think of two steps she could complete while she's still taking classes. Then show how she will continue to work toward her goal. Add more steps to the diagram if you need more.

After your group has filled in the steps, share your ideas with another group. Combine your best ideas. Then present your steps to the class.

Exercise 51   Evaluation   Building Trust at Work

Name _____ Date _____

Read how Samuel did his job one day at a copying service center. List the things he did that might make his supervisor trust him. Then list any of his actions that might make his supervisor not trust him.

Samuel got to work on time and went right to his work station. He looked through the copying jobs he was supposed to do that day. Then he arranged them from the easiest to the hardest. He realized that he probably wouldn't finish them all. He decided to let the employee who worked the evening shift do the hardest jobs.

Samuel finished the first two jobs. He put them neatly in labeled envelopes for the customers. Then it was his break time. He went to the employees' workroom and called his girlfriend. He had to take an extra five minutes for his break. He needed the time to explain to his girlfriend why he had not called her the night before.

Then Samuel went back to work. His supervisor brought over a rush order that Samuel took care of right away. Then Samuel decided that he needed an extra break. He went back to the workroom and called his girlfriend again.

By quitting time, Samuel had three jobs left to do. He left them for the employee who worked the evening shift.

1. Samuel might gain his supervisor's trust because he:

_____

_____

_____

_____

_____

_____

2. Samuel might lose his supervisor's trust because he:

_____

_____

_____

_____

_____

Exercise 52 Evaluation   Rating Yourself

Name _____ Date _____

Fill out your own review for your job as a student.

_____ School

Student: _____   Date: _____
Year/Grade: _____   Review: ___9-Week___

	Needs Improvement	Average	Above Average
1. Attends class every day on time			
2. Has a positive attitude toward school			
3. Studies at least one hour before major tests			
4. Completes work that is assigned			
5. Asks for help when necessary			
6. Works to the best of his or her abilities			
7. Relates well to other students			
8. Follows school rules			
9. Takes part in school activities			
10. Shows respect for teachers and staff			

11. Work with a partner to decide which of the numbered statements might be on a real job review. Write the numbers below.

_____

_____

_____

_____

Exercise 53   Analysis   Analyzing Quotes about Work

Name _____ Date _____

Read the quotations below. Then answer the questions.

1. All of the quotations below relate to working. Read them with a partner, and circle the one you both like best.

    • A good horse should be seldom spurred.   *Thomas Fuller*

    • To be successful, the first thing to do is fall in love with your work.
                                                    Sister Mary Lauretta

    • Most people like hard work, particularly when they're paying for it.
                                                    Franklin P. Jones

    • No race can prosper till it learns there is as much dignity in tilling a field as in writing a poem.   *Booker T. Washington*

    • When I am busy with little things, I am not required to do great things.
                                                    St. Francis de Sales

2. Why did you like the quotation you circled?

    _____

    _____

    _____

    _____

3. What does the quotation mean?

    _____

    _____

    _____

    _____

4. What does this quotation tell you about making the most of your job?

    _____

    _____

    _____

    _____

Exercise 54   Synthesis

Setting Bank Rules

Name _____ Date _____

Pretend that your group is setting up a new bank. Decide which of the fees below you would charge. Remember, if your fees are too high, you won't have any customers. If your fees are too low, the bank won't make any money and might go out of business. Choose fees that you think would be fair.

Then compare your fees with those of other groups. If you had to choose a bank, which group's bank would you choose? Discuss why you would choose that bank with your group members.

Type of fee	If so, how much?
Will a customer have to have a minimum deposit to open an account? Yes No	
Will you pay interest on checking accounts? Yes No	
Will you charge a fee to print customers' names and addresses on their checks? Yes No	
Will you charge a monthly fee to keep customers' accounts open? Yes No	
Will you charge a fee for each check customers write? Yes No	
Will you charge a fee if the money in a customer's account drops below a certain amount? Yes No	
Will you charge customers a fee to use the bank's ATM machines? Yes No	
What other fees will you charge? _____	

Exercise 55   Application

Writing Checks

Name _____   Date _____

Read the information and fill in each check.

1. Susan needs to pay for some groceries she is buying at SuperStore. The total is $23.69. Pretend you are Susan and fill out the check.

```
┌──────────────────────────────────────────────────────────────────────┐
│                                                              143       │
│   Susan Kellner                                                        │
│   3 Home Street                                                        │
│   Cincinnati, OH  34567          Date _____ 19 ____   55-555/1234  │
│                                                             7654321    │
│   PAY TO THE                                                           │
│   ORDER OF _____ │ $ [          ]         │
│                                                                        │
│   _____ DOLLARS              │
│                                                                        │
│   SOUND SURE BANK                                                      │
│   1 Corporate Square                                                   │
│   Cincinnati, OH 34567                                                 │
│                                                                        │
│   MEMO _____   _____             │
│         ⑆061788⑆ 000 ⑈ 0823104⑈                                        │
└──────────────────────────────────────────────────────────────────────┘
```

2. Susan also needs to write a check to her brother, Ken Kellner. She had borrowed $45 from Ken and is paying him back. Fill in this check as Susan would.

```
┌──────────────────────────────────────────────────────────────────────┐
│                                                              144       │
│   Susan Kellner                                                        │
│   3 Home Street                                                        │
│   Cincinnati, OH  34567          Date _____ 19 ____   55-555/1234  │
│                                                             7654321    │
│   PAY TO THE                                                           │
│   ORDER OF _____ │ $ [          ]         │
│                                                                        │
│   _____ DOLLARS              │
│                                                                        │
│   SOUND SURE BANK                                                      │
│   1 Corporate Square                                                   │
│   Cincinnati, OH 34567                                                 │
│                                                                        │
│   MEMO _____   _____             │
│         ⑆061788⑆ 000 ⑈ 0823104⑈                                        │
└──────────────────────────────────────────────────────────────────────┘
```

Exercise 56   Application   Making a Deposit s

Name _____ Date _____

Read the information below and answer the questions.

1. Susan wants to make a bank deposit. She is going to deposit her paycheck of $78.90, plus $23.50 in cash that she earned baby-sitting. She is not going to keep any cash. Fill out her deposit slip for her.

```
DEPOSIT TICKET

Susan Kellner
3 Home Street
Cincinnati, OH  34567

Date _____ 19 _____
DEPOSITS MAY NOT BE AVAILABLE FOR IMMEDIATE WITHDRAWAL

SIGN HERE FOR CASH RECEIVED (IF REQUIRED)

SOUND SURE BANK
1 Corporate Square
Cincinnati, OH  34567

⑆081788⑆ 000 ⑊ 0823194911⑈
CHECKS AND OTHER ITEMS RECEIVED FOR DEPOSIT ARE SUBJECT TO THE PROVISIONS OF THE UNIFORM COMMERICAL OR ANY APPLICABLE COLLECTION AGREEMENT
```

CASH | CURRENCY / COIN
LIST CHECKS SINGLY
55-555/1234
7654321
TOTAL
LESS CASH RECEIVED
NET DEPOSIT
BE SURE EACH ITEM IS PROPERLY ENDORSED
DEPOSIT TICKET
Please itemize additional checks on reverse side

2. Suppose Susan didn't baby-sit this week and is just depositing her paycheck of $78.90. She wants to keep $20 in cash from her paycheck. How would she fill out the deposit slip differently?

```
DEPOSIT TICKET

Susan Kellner
3 Home Street
Cincinnati, OH  34567

Date _____ 19 _____
DEPOSITS MAY NOT BE AVAILABLE FOR IMMEDIATE WITHDRAWAL

SIGN HERE FOR CASH RECEIVED (IF REQUIRED)

SOUND SURE BANK
1 Corporate Square
Cincinnati, OH  34567

⑆081788⑆ 000 ⑊ 0823194911⑈
CHECKS AND OTHER ITEMS RECEIVED FOR DEPOSIT ARE SUBJECT TO THE PROVISIONS OF THE UNIFORM COMMERICAL OR ANY APPLICABLE COLLECTION AGREEMENT
```

CASH | CURRENCY / COIN
LIST CHECKS SINGLY
55-555/1234
7654321
TOTAL
LESS CASH RECEIVED
NET DEPOSIT
BE SURE EACH ITEM IS PROPERLY ENDORSED
DEPOSIT TICKET
Please itemize additional checks on reverse side

Exercise 57 Application   **Keeping a Check Register**

Name _____ Date _____

Susan knows she must use the check register to keep track of the money in her checking account. If she doesn't, she won't know how much money she has in her account. Pretend you are Susan. Fill in her check register below, recording check 143 for $23.69 made out to SuperStore on 6/30/97, check 144 for $45 made out to her brother Ken Kellner on 7/4/97, and Susan's bank deposit of $102.40 made on 7/15/97.

		PLEASE BE SURE TO DEDUCT ANY CHECK CHARGES OR SERVICE CHARGES THAT MAY APPLY TO YOUR ACCOUNT					
NUMBER	DATE	CHECKS ISSUED TO OR DESCRIPTION OF DEPOSIT	(—) AMOUNT OF CHECK	✔ T	(—) CHECK FEE (IF ANY)	(+) AMOUNT OF DEPOSIT	BALANCE 253.64
141	6/19/97	TO/FOR Phone Company	$41.67				$41.67
							BAL $211.97
142	6/22/97	TO/FOR deposit				$78.90	$78.90
							BAL $290.87
		TO/FOR					
							BAL
		TO/FOR					
							BAL
		TO/FOR					
							BAL
		TO/FOR					
							BAL

Now answer these questions.

1. Before Susan wrote check 141, was her balance higher or lower than $211.97? Explain your answer.

    _____

2. What is Sue's balance on 7/15/97?

    _____

3. Some check registers include a column marked "Fee, if any." What kinds of fees might this refer to?

    _____

4. Suppose you recorded one of the fees you listed for question 3 in your check register. Would you add the amount of the fee to your balance or subtract it from your balance? Why?

    _____

Exercise 58   Synthesis   Writing a Letter of Advice

Name _____ Date _____

Imagine you received a letter from your cousin Eric, who lives in another state. He is asking for your advice about managing his money. Write back to Eric, offering some sound advice about managing his money.

Dear Cousin,

    I can't decide whether to put my money in a checking account or a savings account.

    I make about $63.50 a week working part-time during the school year. I share a car with my brother and pay half of the payments and insurance. That comes to about $180 a month. I spend about $15 a week on movies and snacks after school.

    What do you think? Should I put my paycheck into a savings account? I know I would get more interest there.

Sincerely,

Eric

Dear Eric,

_____

_____

_____

_____

_____

_____

_____

_____

_____

_____

_____

_____

Exercise 59 Analysis   Analyzing a Paycheck

Name _____ Date _____

Here is a check that Erin received for working at Sydney's Deli. Look it over carefully. Then answer the questions below.

Sydney's Deli	DATE: 07/23/97 CHECK NO. 1248
24 Broad Street	AMOUNT
Albany, TN 33456	$201.25

PAY **Erin Connor**

TO THE ORDER OF **Two hundred and One** $\frac{25}{100}$ **DOLLARS**

SECOND CITY BANK
1 Clarkson Drive
Albany, TN 33460

AUTHORIZED SIGNATURE *Sydney Varner*
ACCOUNTANT

⑃061788⑃ 000 ⑈ 0823104⑈

Circle True or False for each statement. Then explain your choices.

1. *True*   *False*   Erin lives at 24 Broad Street in Albany, TN. Explain your answer. _____

   _____

2. *True*   *False*   Erin must cash this check by July 23. Explain your answer.

   _____

3. *True*   *False*   Sydney Varner signed this check. Explain your answer.

   _____

4. *True*   *False*   Sydney's Deli keeps its money at Second City Bank.

   Explain your answer. _____

   _____

5. *True*   *False*   Because $201.25 is written on this check twice, the check can be cashed for $402.50. Explain your answer.

   _____

6. *True*   *False*   Erin wrote in the $201.25 amount. Explain your answer.

   _____

Exercise 60   Analysis   Understanding a Paycheck Stub

Name _____ Date _____

Below is Erin's paycheck stub. She makes $6 an hour at Sydney's Deli. Study her paycheck stub carefully and answer the questions.

EMPLOYEE NAME	EMPLOYEE ID					SYDNEY'S DELI
Connor, Erin	234-98-1009					24 Broad Street Albany, TN 33456

ISSUE DATE	PAY PERIOD ENDING
07/23/97	07/20/97

Earnings Description	Hours	Current	YTD	Deductions Descriptions	Currents	YTD
Weekly pay	40	240.00	2030.00	FICA	18.36	155.30
				FIT	15.67	123.89
				State Tax	2.32	31.68
				City Tax	2.40	20.39
				Net Pay		201.25

STATEMENTS OF EARNINGS AND DEDUCTIONS • DETACH AND RETAIN FOR YOUR RECORDS

1. How many different kinds of taxes were taken out of Erin's paycheck?

   _____

2. Find 2030.00 under the heading YTD. What is this amount?

   _____

3. How much state tax has been deducted from Erin's pay so far this year?

   _____

4. If she had worked 20 hours instead of 40, what would the number be under the current heading?

   _____

5. After the deductions are subtracted, is Erin's net pay of $201.25 correct? How do you know?

   _____

Exercise 61   Synthesis   Writing a Letter of Advice

Name _____ Date _____

Imagine that you and a partner write an advice column for a teen magazine. It's called "Advice from Andy." A reader wrote the letter shown below to you. He wants your advice.

Dear Andy,

    I'm really angry. No one respects teenagers in my town. This afternoon I got my first paycheck from the grocery store where I work. I took it straight to the nearest bank. Do you know what? The teller wouldn't cash it! What can I do to get my check cashed?

Your friend,

Chris

Work with your partner to write back to Chris. Where might Chris go to get his check cashed? What might he do to help this situation before he gets his next check?

Dear Chris,

_____

_____

_____

_____

_____

_____

_____

_____

_____

_____

_____

_____

_____

Exercise 62   Evaluation   Sorting Out Expenses

Name _____ Date _____

Tony needs your help in setting up his budget. Read below to see how much he earns and how much he spends. Then list his expenses and his income.

"I just got a new job. I also just got a new car. My mom made the down payment on the car, but I have to make the monthly payments. They're $125 a month! Then there's my car insurance. I can't avoid that, no matter how much I'd like to. The insurance payment is due every six months and is about $500.

"Even just having fun costs money. My girlfriend loves to go to the movies. One week she pays; the next week I do. We usually get something to eat afterwards. It costs me at least $20 when it's my turn to pay.

"I forgot about gas for my car. So far, that's about $20 a week. But I figure I can keep it down to $15 if I try.

"I work about 15 hours a week after school. I make $5.50 an hour clearing tables at a restaurant. But my paycheck isn't $82.50. It's only about $65 after taxes.

"So what do you think? Will I have enough money each month? Or should I start looking for a second job?"

1. Tony's Monthly Income   Tony's Monthly Expenses

     _____

     _____

     _____

     _____

     _____

2. Figure out whether Tony's income will cover his expenses. Tell him what you discovered.

     _____

     _____

     _____

3. Give Tony some advice about balancing his budget.

     _____

     _____

     _____

Exercise 63 Application   Calculating Income

Name _____ Date _____

Marney has just gotten a new part-time job. She will work 20 hours per week. Her pay is $5.00 per hour. She wanted to know what her net pay would be. She asked her boss, and he gave her the following information.

Each week the following deductions will be taken out of Marney's paycheck:

Federal tax   20% of gross pay
State tax   5% of gross pay
Social Security tax   7.5% of gross pay
City tax   1.5% of gross pay

1. How much money will be deducted each week for each tax?

   Federal tax _____

   State tax _____

   Social Security tax _____

   City tax _____

2. What will Marney's net pay be each week? _____

3. Marney needs $55.00 each week to cover her expenses. She would like to save enough money to buy a new dress for the prom. The dress costs $120.00, and the prom is 15 weeks away. Will Marney be able to save enough to buy the dress?

   _____

   _____

   _____

4. Marney's friend tells her about another job. It pays $6.00 per hour. The same percentages would be deducted from her check each week for taxes. She could work 20 hours per week. Should Marney take the job? Explain why you think she should or should not.

   _____

   _____

   _____

   _____

Exercise 64 Application   **Shopping Carefully**

Name _____ Date _____

Suppose you have $100 to spend on clothes. See how much you can get for that $100. Use store catalogs, store flyers, or newspaper ads to find clothing that you like. If possible, cut out pictures of the items you chose, plus their prices. Paste or describe them below. Make sure the total cost of the clothing under each heading is no more than $100.

Here's how much I could buy for $100:

Answer the following questions based on what you found.

1. Should you always buy the least expensive clothing you can find? Why or why not?

   _____

   _____

   _____

2. What are some good reasons to buy one shirt that costs more than another shirt?

   _____

   _____

   _____

3. What are some good reasons *not* to buy the most expensive brand of something, such as jeans?

   _____

   _____

   _____

Exercise 65 Analysis

Comparing Messages

Name _____ Date _____

Different products can be advertised by using the same message. Look at the advertising messages below. Look through magazines and newspapers for ads that use those messages. Choose two very different products that are being advertised with the same message. Then answer the question.

1. *Everybody else has one.* Does an ad using this message make you want to buy the product?

   _____

   _____

2. *Famous people use this product.* Does an ad using this message make you want to buy the product?

   _____

   _____

3. *This product will make you look more attractive.* Does an ad using this message make you want to buy the product?

   _____

   _____

4. *Use this product and you'll have more fun.* Does an ad using this message make you want to buy the product?

   _____

   _____

5. *We are your friends; you can trust us.* Does an ad using this message make you want to buy the product?

   _____

   _____

Exercise 66   Application   Designing an Ad

Name _____ Date _____

Ads can make almost anything look good. They can sometimes make you want something you normally wouldn't like. The more you know about advertising messages, the better prepared you will be to resist them.

1. Look around the classroom or your home and find something that you don't like.

2. Design an ad to sell that product, in whatever condition it's in. In your ad, turn any weakness of your product into a selling point. For example, you might be trying to sell a pencil that has been chewed. Your ad might say that the tooth marks show the pencil has many uses, including reducing tension.

3. Try out different ads for your product on scrap paper.

4. Then put your best ad below.

5. Share your ad and product with a small group. Discuss times when you have heard a real salesperson try to turn a product's weakness into a selling point.

Exercise 67   Application   Writing Tips for Consumers

Name _____ Date _____

Just for fun, list five or six tips that would help someone spend a lot of money at the grocery store and still not get what he or she needed. Don't list good tips, like "Before you go to the store, make a list of what you need." Instead, you might write something like this: "When you get to the store, wander around and look for interesting things."

Tip 1: _____

Tip 2: _____

Tip 3: _____

Tip 4: _____

Tip 5: _____

Tip 6: _____

After writing your tips, answer the following questions.

1. If someone followed your tips, what would be the result?

   _____

   _____

   _____

2. Which tips have you followed without realizing it?

   _____

   _____

   _____

3. Why do you think some people follow your tips without realizing it?

   _____

   _____

   _____

Then read your tips to the class and discuss what is wrong with each tip.

Exercise 68   Evaluation   Judging Actions

Name _____ Date _____

Tanisha is angry. She may have caused part of the problem herself. Read what happened and answer the questions.

Tonya's birthday was in three weeks, so her sister Tanisha bought her a nice pair of jeans. Tonya was excited when she opened her present and saw the jeans. Yet when she tried them on, she didn't like the way they looked on her. "Don't worry," Tanisha said. "I'll take them back and get you something else."

Tanisha searched for the sales slip for the jeans, but she couldn't find it. However, she took the jeans back to the store anyway.

The clerk said the store would take back the jeans, even though Tanisha didn't have the sales slip. However, the jeans were on sale for much less than Tanisha had paid. The store would only refund the sales price. Tanisha said she had bought the jeans three weeks ago, before the sale.

Tanisha had spent all her money on Tonya's present. If she got a refund for the sale price, she couldn't buy Tonya something else that was as nice. But if she didn't return the jeans, she'd end up giving Tonya nothing! Tanisha thought about keeping the jeans for herself, but they didn't fit her at all. What a waste!

1. What was Tanisha's main mistake?

   _____

   _____

2. What other mistake did Tanisha make?

   _____

   _____

3. Do you think the clerk was right to offer to refund only the sale price of the jeans? Why or why not?

   _____

   _____

4. Do you think the clerk would have been right to refuse to take back the jeans at all? Why or why not?

   _____

   _____

Exercise 69   Analysis   Examining a Bill

Name _____ Date _____

Below is part of a telephone bill Greg received last month. Study it and then answer the questions.

CONSUMER SERVICES Billing Summary	613 555-8720 July 1, 1997

Previous Bill	Payments	Adjustments	Past Due Amount	Current Charges	Total Amount Due
71.77	0.00	0.00	71.77	51.37	123.14

Summary of Current Charges
Ameritech

Monthly Services	25.45
Local Calls	.75
Local and State Additional Charges	.12
Federal Taxes	.79
Total Ameritech Current Charges	27.11
ABC Long Distance Company	
Long distance charges	24.26
Total Current Charges	**$51.37**

1. How much of last month's phone bill did Greg pay?

   _____

2. Why is the Total Amount Due higher than the Current Charges?

   _____

3. Greg still can't afford to pay his phone bill. He decides he won't pay it this month. He also decides that he won't make any more long distance phone calls. How much is his phone bill likely to be next month, even if the phone company does not add an interest charge or late fee?

   _____

4. What does Greg risk if he doesn't pay his phone bill?

   _____

Exercise 70 Analysis   Analyzing Credit Card Bills

Name _____ Date _____

This is the credit card bill that Amanda just received for one of her credit cards. Study the bill and use it to answer the questions.

Rossman's Department Store **518 Galena Avenue** **Albany, WI 53502**	**Closing Date:** September 30 **Payment Due:** October 15

Account Summary
Account Number	6011 2002 5641
Credit Limit	$400.00
Credit Available	$ 75.60
Minimum Payment	$ 35.00

Previous Balance	$240.62
Payments & Credits	30.00
New Purchases	109.85
FINANCE CHARGES	3.93
New Balance	$324.40

Transactions
Payments and Credits
Sept. 10	Payment – Thank You	30.00

Purchases
Sept. 18	Ladies Sportswear	$99.32
Sept. 18	Cosmetics	10.53

- -

Please detach and return with your payment.

Account Number   6011 2002 5641   Minimum Payment $35.00   New Balance $324.00

Amanda Ruez 850 Pine Street Albany, WI 53502	**Payment** **Enclosed** $_____

1. What is Amanda's minimum payment? When is it due?

   _____

   _____

2. Did Amanda buy anything with her credit card at Rossman's in the past month? How do you know?

   _____

   _____

Exercise 71   Analysis   Comparing Credit Cards

Name _____ Date _____

Work with a group to compare credit cards. Fill out the chart below for as many of the credit cards as possible. You might gather this information by talking to people who have the cards or by calling banks or stores that offer the credit cards. If you wish, add another type of credit card. Figure out which credit card company has the best offer.

| Type of Card | Annual Fee | | Interest Rate | Place Where This Card Is Accepted |
	Yes (How Much?)	No		
MasterCard				
Visa				
American Express				
Discover				
_____ (Card from a large store)				
_____ (Card from a small store)				
_____ (Gas Station Card)				

Answer the following questions using the information you gathered.

1. Which card, if any, would your group recommend for a teenager? Explain your choice.

   _____

   _____

2. Besides the information above, what else, should you consider when choosing a credit card?

   _____

   _____

Exercise 72   Analysis   Analyzing Ads

Name _____ Date _____

Being a responsible consumer isn't easy sometimes. Companies often call or write to people, trying to get them to apply for a credit card. Some companies send credit cards to people who haven't even applied for them. On the applications, interest charges and annual fees are usually explained in tiny print.

Collect several credit card advertisements. Many times the ads can be found with the card application forms. Work with a partner to analyze advertising claims of credit card companies. Beside each claim listed below, write the truth.

The credit card company says	But you know
1. Get the things you want, when you want them!	
2. Low monthly payments!	
3. Why wait? Start using your new credit card today!	
4. Charge up to $1,500 without paying a cent!	

Exercise 73   Synthesis   Creating an Ad

Name _____ Date _____

Answer the questions below.

1. List three reasons for people to take the bus or subway instead of driving.

   a. _____

   b. _____

   c. _____

2. On another sheet of paper, make a poster to encourage people to take the bus or subway. As you plan your poster, use one of the reasons you listed above. Also, think about the ad messages you have learned about earlier. You might be able to use one of them in your poster. Share your poster with the class.

3. Discuss the questions below with the class.

   a. How did listing the reasons for taking a bus or subway help you create an effective poster?

   _____

   _____

   _____

   b. Look at the class's posters. Which reasons to take the bus or subway were used most often? Why do you think this is so?

   _____

   _____

   _____

   c. What might your community do to encourage more people to use public transportation?

   _____

   _____

   _____

Exercise 74 Analysis   Reading a Bus Schedule

Name _____ Date _____

Before you take a bus, you have to be able to read a bus schedule. Study the schedule shown below. The times listed in the white boxes are in the morning. The times in the gray boxes are in the afternoon. See if you can answer the questions.

Stops on Monday-Friday: Going North				
City Center Terminal	Broad & High St.	Cleveland & Innis St.	Cleveland & 161 St.	Bus
6:20	6:23	6:43	6:52	A
7:04	7:07	7:28	7:37	B
7:23	7:26			C
7:34	7:38			D
7:52	7:56			E
8:14	8:18			F
8:59	9:03			G
3:41	3:45	4:05	4:15	A
4:37	4:41	5:05	5:13	B
4:49	4:55	5:17	5:29	C
5:13	5:19	5:43	5:52	D
5:37	5:41	6:03	6:12	E
6:13	6:17	6:38	6:47	F

1. Why are there no times for Buses C through G for two of the stops?

    _____

2. Let's say you caught the 7:07 bus in the morning at Broad and High. You are traveling north to your job at Cleveland and Innis. Would a later morning bus also bring you to work? Why or why not?

    _____

3. If you were at the corner of Cleveland and 161 at 5:20 in the afternoon, how long would you have to wait for a bus?

    _____

4. What is the latest time in the morning that you could catch a bus going north from the City Center terminal?

    _____

Exercise 75   Analysis

Understanding Signs

Name _____ Date _____

Could you pass the written driver's license test? The questions below are like the ones on the test. Circle the letter that tells what each sign means.

1.

    a. Sharp turn to the right ahead

    b. Sharp turn to the left ahead

    c. Crossroad ahead

2.

    a. You must ride a bicycle here.

    b. Watch out for people riding bicycles here.

    c. Riding a bicycle is good exercise.

3.

    a. Stop here and check to see if any cars are coming.

    b. Go slowly here.

    c. Other cars will stop for you, so you can keep going.

4.

    a. Don't drive here.

    b. Crossroad ahead

    c. Railroad crossing ahead

Exercise 76   Analysis

Using a Graph

Name _____ Date _____

The graph below helps explain why car insurance rates are higher for teenagers. The numbers show how many deaths from car accidents there are for every 100,000 drivers in each age group. Study the graph below and then answer the questions. Compare your answers with a partner's answers.

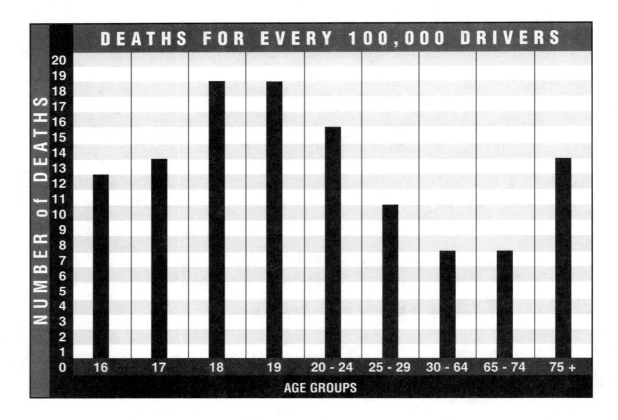

1. Which age groups have the most deaths from traffic accidents? Which age groups have the fewest deaths from traffic accidents?

   _____

2. Look at the 16-year-old age group. Out of every 100,000, how many 16-year-olds die each year from traffic accidents?

   _____

3. Why do you think insurance rates are higher for teenage drivers?

   _____

Exercise 77   Application   Recognizing Responsible Behavior

Name _____ Date _____

Read each situation below. Then decide what you think a responsible driver might do. Share your ideas with the class.

1. Jamal is driving to school. He is worried about being late. He needs to make a left turn onto Oak Street. He has to turn across the oncoming traffic lane. A car is coming toward him, so he waits for it to pass. Then he sees another car coming toward him. This car is about half a block away. What would a responsible driver do in Jamal's situation? Remember, he might be late for school unless he hurries.

   _____

   _____

   _____

   _____

2. Andrea is driving home. It will take her 15 more minutes to get there. She is really tired, and her eyes keep closing. What would a responsible driver do in Andrea's situation?

   _____

   _____

   _____

3. Mike's old car needs new brakes. Lately, he has had to push on the brake pedal very hard to get the car to stop. However, his friends are going to a concert this weekend. If Mike fixes his car, he won't be able to buy a ticket for the concert. What would a responsible driver do in Mike's situation?

   _____

   _____

   _____

   _____

Exercise 78 Evaluation   **Comparing Housing**

Name _____ Date _____

Choosing the best housing for yourself can be confusing. To sort out the choices, work with a partner to complete the chart below. Then answer the questions.

Housing Choice	Evaluation
Living at home	Advantages: Disadvantages:
Renting a room in someone else's house	Advantages: Disadvantages:
Renting an apartment with a roommate	Advantages: Disadvantages:

1. What do you think is the best housing choice for people who have just graduated from high school? Explain your answer.

   _____

   _____

2. Why do you think many young people rush to get an apartment of their own?

   _____

   _____

3. To have your own apartment, you must be able to pay the rent. What other things do young people need to be able to do before they are ready to live on their own?

   _____

   _____

Exercise 79   Application   **Writing an Ad**

Name _____ Date _____

Imagine that the McCabe family lives in a large house down the street from you. Last year, their oldest daughter moved out of the house and into her own apartment. She is doing well there, so the McCabes have decided to rent out her room.

Mrs. McCabe has asked for your help. She wants you to write a classified newspaper ad for the room. Begin by reviewing the classified ads in your newspaper. Keep your ad short and use some of the same abbreviations as in the newspaper ads. Be sure to tell readers how to contact Mrs. McCabe.

ROOMS FOR RENT
_____
_____
_____
_____
_____
_____

Share your ad with a group. Then answer and discuss the questions below.

1. Which of the group's ads are likely to get calls from interested renters? Why ?

    _____

    _____

2. What are some things about a room for rent that are not likely to be included in an ad? One example: the renter must share a bathroom with a family of 13.

    _____

    _____

3. What has writing these ads taught you about reading real ads in the newspaper?

    _____

    _____

Exercise 80 Evaluation   Deciding on Housing

Name _____ Date _____

When people choose a place to live, they have certain needs and wants. Often their needs and wants change as they grow older. Read this list of things to consider in choosing housing.

Now pretend you are looking for a new place to live. Use the items in the list on the left to write your own list. Put your most important need or want at the top and your least important need or want at the bottom. Then fill in the other things in order of importance to you. Compare your written list with a partner's. Discuss why you put things in that order.

Possible Things to Consider: **My List:**

Location (near work or bus line)   Most important to me: _____

Cost of the housing   _____

Size of the room or apartment   _____

Safety features   _____

Furnishings   _____

Laundry facilities   _____

Age of the housing   _____

Ages of others who live there   _____

Parking   _____

Storage for bikes   Least important to me: _____

What other things would you consider when choosing a place to live? Explain your answer.

_____

_____

_____

_____

_____

Exercise 81   Analysis   Understanding a Rental Agreement

Name _____ Date _____

An apartment rental agreement, or lease, is shown below. Study it with a partner. Then answer the questions below about it.

RENTAL AGREEMENT

Apple Apartments agrees to rent apartment #24A to Jason Samuels, who is referred to below as "the renter."

The rental period will begin on July 1, 1997 and continue until June 30, 1998. Apple Apartments or the renter may end this agreement by giving 30 days notice, in writing.

The renter agrees to pay a one-time security deposit of $400 and an additional $400 per month for each month of this agreement. Rent for each month must be paid by the first day of that month. Mail rent checks to Apple Apartments, 49 East Orange Road, Lansing, MI 12345.

The renter is responsible for electricity and phone service. Apple Apartments will pay for water and garbage collection.

The renter must follow these rules:

1. Do not keep any pets in the apartment.
2. Do not paint the walls or ceilings.
3. To hang things on the walls, use hooks available in the rental office.
4. Make no loud noise, especially between 10:00 P.M. and 8:00 A.M.
5. Park only in your assigned spot.

_____   _____
Carrie Newsome   The renter
Apple Apartments Rental Agent

---

1. When is Jason's rent for August due?

_____

2. Suppose Jason gets a new job and must move to another city at the end of November. When should he tell Apple Apartments he is moving?

_____

3. Jason likes to take long, hot showers. Will his showers add to the cost of his apartment?

_____

4. What does Jason have to do if he wants to hang his baseball cap collection on the wall?

_____

Exercise 82 Application   Sorting Out Social Security

Name _____ Date _____

Do you understand the purpose of your Social Security number? Answer the questions below. Then discuss the questions as a class.

1. How many people have the same Social Security number that you do? **Explain your answer.**

   _____

   _____

   _____

2. When you apply for a Social Security card, what will you have to do?

   _____

   _____

   _____

3. Let's say you have a new job. However, you accidentally wrote the wrong Social Security number on your job application form. What problems will this cause?

   _____

   _____

   _____

4. What are some reasons you should not give your Social Security number to people who call you on the telephone?

   _____

   _____

   _____

5. Suppose the government changed the law and you no longer had to pay Social Security taxes. How would this change affect you now and in the future?

   _____

   _____

   _____

Exercise 83   Analysis   Understanding Voting

Name _____ Date _____

Help these young people become good citizens. Read each situation below and answer the questions.

1. It's August, and Nancy is going to the town library to register to vote. Her family is moving to another state in September. Nancy wants to register now so she can vote in the November elections.

   a. Will Nancy be able to vote in her new state in the November elections? Why or why not?

   _____

   _____

   _____

   b. What should Nancy do if she wants to vote in November?

   _____

   _____

   _____

2. It's almost time to elect a new mayor. Amelia has heard one television commercial over and over. The commercial says that one candidate for mayor is going to raise everyone's taxes. Amelia doesn't want to pay higher taxes. She decides to vote for the other candidate.

   a. Is Amelia making a wise decision? Why or why not?

   _____

   _____

   _____

   b. What are some other things that Amelia should find out before she votes?

   _____

   _____

   _____

Exercise 84 Synthesis

Writing a Letter to the Editor

Name _____ Date _____

Imagine you and your partner like to read the letters to the editor in your newspaper. Lately, several writers have complained about paying taxes.

In the space below, work with your partner to write a letter to the editor. Tell newspaper readers why people pay taxes. Explain what could happen if people stopped paying taxes. You might also suggest things that people could do if they don't like the ways their tax money is being spent.

Dear Editor:

_____

_____

_____

_____

_____

_____

_____

_____

_____

_____

_____

_____

_____

_____

_____

_____

_____

Exercise 85 Analysis   Figuring Out Taxes

Name _____   Date _____

Imagine you have been asked to help the people below to do their taxes. Read each situation and answer the questions. Use the space below each question to show your math.

1. Ned's W-2 form shows that he earned $13,500 last year and that his employer withheld $1,200 for federal income taxes. Ned figured out that he actually owes $1,065 in federal income tax. He decides to send the government a check for the difference between the two numbers: $135.

   a. What mistake is Ned making?

   _____

   _____

   b. What should Ned do about his taxes?

   _____

   _____

2. KC and her husband can file one tax form together, or they can each file a separate tax return. They each earned $17,000 this year. Here are the tax rates:

Tax Rate for Married Couples Who File a Tax Return Together	
15%	$0 to $39,000 in total income
28%	$39,001 to $94,250 in total income
Tax Rate for Married Couples Who File Separate Tax Returns	
15%	$0 to $19,500 each in income
28%	$19,501 to $47,125 each in income

   a. What is the tax rate for KC and her husband if they file a tax return together? If they each file a separate return?

   _____

   _____

   b. If a married couple files separate tax returns, they each get a standard deduction of $3,500. If they file a tax return together, they get a standard deduction for a married couple of $6,550. Should KC and her husband file together or separately?

   _____

   _____

Exercise 86 Synthesis   Writing a Letter of Advice

Name _____ Date _____

Pretend that you received the letter below from your friend Kia, who lives in another state.

Dear Friend,

    I am so angry! I got my first speeding ticket today. The police officer said I was going 44 miles per hour, but the speed limit was 35 on that street.

    I was in a hurry to pick up my brother Robbie after his Boy Scout meeting. I was just trying to get there on time. Is that so terrible?

    Why do the police care how fast you're driving, anyway? I think you should be allowed to drive as fast as you think is safe. I know how good a driver I am, so I know how fast I can drive.

    Now I have to pay a $65 fine! That's all the money I've got. I hope this never happens to you!

Your friend,

Kia

Write Kia a letter. You can sympathize with her anger, but help her understand why drivers aren't allowed to go as fast as they want to.

Dear Kia,

_____

_____

_____

_____

_____

_____

_____

_____

_____

_____

Exercise 87   Analysis   Thinking about School Rules

Name _____ Date _____

Laws for drivers, bike riders, and walkers are designed to keep them and others safe. Schools also have rules to keep students and employees safe.

1. With a group, think of some school or business rules that are designed to keep you safe. Write them in the chart below. Explain how each rule helps protect students or employees. Include rules you are asked to follow inside and outside your school or job.

Rule	How It Keeps You Safe

2. Share your group's list of rules with the class. List each different rule on the board.

3. Discuss the following questions as a class:

   a. Do the rules the class listed deal mainly with one kind of problem? If so, why and what is it?

   _____

   _____

   b. Which rule do you think could be eliminated? Why?

   _____

   _____

   c. What new rule would you add? Why?

   _____

   _____

Exercise 88   Application   Designing a Poster

Name _____ Date _____

With a group, choose a law that is frequently violated in your community. You could call your police department and ask which laws are violated most often. Don't call 911 to ask. Use the nonemergency number listed in the phone book.

After your group has selected a law, design a poster to encourage people to obey that law. The posters need to convince people that a certain law protects them in some way. After you draw your group's poster in the space below, you might enlarge it for the classroom wall.

After groups share their posters with the class, discuss these questions:

1. What kinds of accidents and injuries do laws help prevent?

    _____

    _____

2. What are some reasons people disobey laws?

    _____

    _____

3. Do laws take away people's rights? If so, is this fair?

    _____

    _____

Exercise 89   Application   Making a Map

Name _____ Date _____

Complete the following activities.

1. Pretend that you are walking, riding a bike, or driving a car from your home to your school. Draw a map of the way you would go. Include the names of the streets.

   Map:

   _____
   | |
   | |
   | |
   | |
   | |
   | |
   | |
   | |
   | |
   | |
   |_____|

2. Now imagine that your community has no traffic laws, traffic signs, or traffic lights. Below, describe some problems you would face on your way to school. Use your map to explain where the problems would happen. For example:

   Problem: When I got to the corner of Oak and Main, I would have trouble

   crossing the street. There would be no traffic light to stop the cars.

   Problem: _____

   _____

   Problem: _____

   _____

   Problem: _____

   _____

Exercise 90   Application   Researching Community Agencies

Name _____ Date _____

With a group, go on a "Help Hunt." Each group will use a phone book to identify agencies that could help with the problems below. Then a member of each group will read the agencies and phone numbers they found to the class.

Groups might list different agencies or phone numbers for the same problem. Discuss these differences. Decide which would be the best agency to call for each problem below.

Problems:

1. I think I should be getting unemployment checks, but I'm not sure.

   Agency: _____   Phone Number: _____

2. My water bill is much higher than usual this month.

   Agency: _____   Phone Number: _____

3. I need a passport.

   Agency: _____   Phone Number: _____

4. I have a question about my federal income tax.

   Agency: _____   Phone Number: _____

5. I'd like to find some fun activities for my grandfather.

   Agency: _____   Phone Number: _____

6. I want to join the Army.

   Agency: _____   Phone Number: _____

7. My neighbor's welfare check is late, and I want to help him.

   Agency: _____   Phone Number: _____

8. My brother wants to get a marriage license.

   Agency: _____   Phone Number: _____

9. My grandmother's Social Security check is late.

   Agency: _____   Phone Number: _____

10. I want to talk to my U.S. Senator.

    Agency: _____   Phone Number: _____

Exercise 91   Analysis   Relaying Messages

Name _____ Date _____

Work with two other people to try out a message relay service. Two people in the group will send messages back and forth with the help of the third "relay" person. The relay person will be the only one who talks.

Here are the steps:

1. The first person will write a message.

2. The relay person will read that message aloud to the third person.

3. The third person will write a response.

4. The relay person will read the third person's response aloud to the first person.

After trying out the relay service, answer these questions:

1. What kinds of communication problems would the relay service help with?

   _____

   _____

   _____

2. What problems did you have in using the service? What are some ways to overcome these problems?

   _____

   _____

   _____

3. How is a relay service similar to computer E-mail? How is it different?

   _____

   _____

   _____

Exercise 92   Analysis   Researching Community Activities

Name _____ Date _____

With a group, list at least three activities in your community that each group below might enjoy. Choose activities that are open to the public and free (or very inexpensive). Begin by listing activities you know about. Then add to your lists by checking the newspaper or your community recreation department.

Preschoolers (babies to age 4):

1. _____

2. _____

3. _____

School-Age Children (ages 5-12):

1. _____

2. _____

3. _____

Teenagers (ages 13-19)

1. _____

2. _____

3. _____

Single Adults (age 20 or older)

1. _____

2. _____

3. _____

When your group's lists are complete, read them to the class. Then discuss these questions.

1. Which activities on the lists are well known and well attended? Why is that?

_____

2. Which group has the least activities available, as far as you know? Do you think this causes problems for that group? Why or why not?

_____